Early Automobiles

THE STORY OF HORSELESS CARRIAGES FROM THE CLOCK-SPRING CAR OF 1649 TO HENRY FORD'S MODEL T

By EUGENE RACHLIS

Illustrated by JACK COGGINS

GOLDEN PRESS 🦢 NEW YORK

Library of Congress Card Catalog Number 61-15012

Cover: *Early Automobile* by Leslie Saalburg, Courtesy of *Esquire.*

Operated by a clock spring, the 1649 Nuremberg car had to be rewound every few minutes.

Man In Motion

In his efforts to move by means other than his own two feet, man has sat on the backs of mules, camels, oxen, horses and elephants, and has been pulled in carts, wagons, carriages and sleds. He has crammed himself into airplanes which exceed the speed of sound and into roller-coasters that only feel that way. He has used boats on water, skis on snow, skates on ice, and bicycles on land. Of all the devices which man has invented to carry him from here to there, swiftly and effortlessly, none has had quite as much impact on his life as the automobile.

All over the world, the automobile industry and the industries which serve it—rubber, steel and other metals, glass, and plastics—provide employment for millions of people. Millions more are at work in the oil industry, in highway construction, and in services which depend entirely on the motorist—motels, gas stations, roadside stores and restaurants, and drive-in movies.

In America, where the automobile has probably had the most profound influence, cars have moved people from the city to the suburbs and have forced department stores and supermarkets to move with them to giant shopping centers with vast parking space. The automobile takes us to school and to work, on pleasure trips and business trips, on long cross-country vacations and on afternoon picnics.

The influence of the automobile on our life has been so complete that few

6

of us can remember what it was like to be without one. Yet it was not so long ago that men first devised the means of mechanical self-propulsion which made the modern car possible. They had tried for hundreds of years to replace manpower or animal power with a mechanical device. None was found workable until late in the nineteenth century.

One of the earliest self-propelled cars was built by clockmakers in Nuremberg, Germany, in 1649. It was operated on the same spring principle as a wind-up toy. Like a toy, it had to be rewound every few minutes.

About fifty years after that, an Englishman named Thomas Savery developed a steam pump which raised water from coal mines. This was improved upon by another Englishman, Thomas Newcomen. In 1765, James Watt of Scotland, using Newcomen's engine as a model, made a steam engine so efficient that he is generally considered to be its inventor. Although these early steam engines operated from a fixed position, they generated power. Watt himself was opposed to using steam power to run a road vehicle, and urged his associates to stop working on such a project. But these and other men with vision saw the possibility of steam power propelling vehicles on land and water.

In Europe and the United States, men began to experiment with steam. The search for an automobile—although it would be years before it carried that name—was on.

James Watt's steam engine, perfected in 1765, made possible the invention of steam cars.

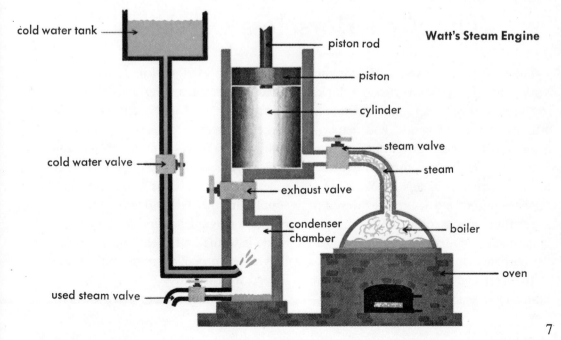

Watt's Steam Engine

cold water tank
piston rod
piston
cylinder
steam valve
steam
cold water valve
exhaust valve
condenser chamber
boiler
oven
used steam valve

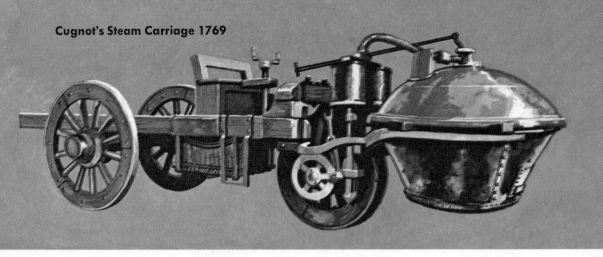

Cugnot's Steam Carriage 1769

Cugnot's 1769 steam carriage was an early experiment in machine-propelled carriages.

The Orukter Amphibolos, developed by Oliver Evans in 1804, was a steam-operated dredging machine with removable wheels and bucket chains on its sides.

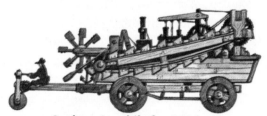

Orukter Amphibolos 1804

The First Horseless Carriages

The man who is given credit for the world's first self-propelled road vehicle is Nicholas Joseph Cugnot, a French artillery officer. Cugnot had experimented with steam propulsion in the 1760's and had come to the attention of the French Minister of War. The minister authorized Cugnot to develop a machine which could replace horses as a means of dragging cannon onto the battlefield.

In 1769 and again in 1770 Cugnot built such a machine—although its mili-

tary value was doubtful. It had three wheels, with an engine and boiler attached to the single front wheel. It looked more like a farm tractor than it did a car. It was a cumbersome, unwieldly vehicle and could go only three miles an hour. What is more, the water supply in the boiler lasted only ten minutes. Cugnot's steam machine never made it to the battlefield, but it proved that a self-propelled road vehicle was indeed a possibility.

For a hundred years after Cugnot,

progress was slow. In England, early in the nineteenth century, several types of steam-driven coaches did pull carriages carrying passengers. By 1830, a good many steam-propelled coaches were operating on regular schedules between London and outlying areas. But they did not represent very much of an improvement over horse-drawn carriages. Eventually, frequent boiler explosions, and the passing of the Red Flag Act (which demanded that each steam-operated vehicle traveling on the highway be preceded by a man waving a red flag of warning), stopped their use in England.

In America, in 1790, Nathan Read built a model for a vehicle which he called "light, strong, compact and dependable, and suitable for use in a steam carriage." But he dropped the project and nothing more was to come of it. Fifteen years later Oliver Evans of Philadelphia built the Orukter Amphibolos, or "amphibious digger." It was a steam dredge which could be converted to a water craft by the removal of its wheels. It dredged quite well, but no one could see in it the prospect of carrying human beings.

Nevertheless, the dream of self-propulsion persisted. Although steam would one day prove itself in automobiles, it was not until men turned to other means of power that they began to come close to their goal.

In 1831, Gurney's steam carriage provided regular transportation between Gloucester and Cheltenham, England, a nine mile trip, in 45 minutes.

Gurney's Steam Carriage

Internal Combustion

The invention which finally made it possible for man to propel himself on wheels economically and speedily was the internal-combustion engine. This phrase is simply a way of saying that the engine gets its power by burning fuel (combustion) within itself (internal). Nowadays the most common fuel used in internal-combustion engines is gasoline, which is refined from crude oil found in the ground. But at the time the first successful internal-combustion engine was built, in 1860, oil had just been discovered and very little was known about it. In fact, gasoline was considered a useless by-product and was thrown away.

Étienne Lenoir, a Belgian who worked in France, used illuminating gas to power this first really workable internal-combustion engine. In 1863 he built a carriage for his engine. And it moved, although not much faster than Cugnot's steam vehicle. It went six miles in an hour and a half.

Soon, others made improvements in the internal-combustion engine. Siegfried Marcus of Vienna produced an automobile in 1864 and a better one in 1875. He, and Lenoir also, did not carry on this work and let others receive the credit for inventing the gasoline automobile. In America, in 1876, George B. Brayton operated an engine at the Philadelphia Centennial Exposition. It had many faults and could not run at more than a very low speed— but it worked.

The internal combustion engine works by the explosion of compressed gas and air.

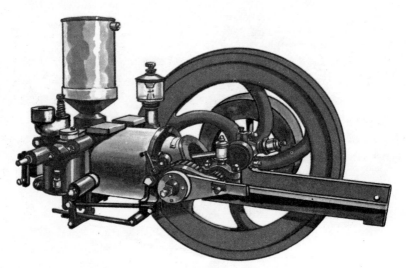

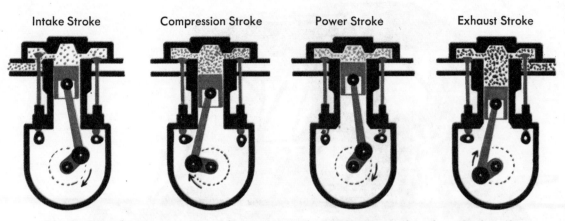

| Intake Stroke | Compression Stroke | Power Stroke | Exhaust Stroke |

The Four-cycle Engine: (1) gasoline vapor and air mixture reaches the cylinder. (2) valve closes and mixture is compressed. (3) spark plug ignites mixture. (4) piston is forced down by the explosion, exhaust is emitted allowing fresh mixture to renew cycle.

Then, in 1877, Nikolaus August Otto, a German engineer, built a four cycle internal-combustion engine. The search for the means of propelling a road vehicle was over. With improvements and refinements, Otto's basic invention has run nearly every automobile that has ever been put on the road, although several two-cycle cars were built then, and are still being made today.

The engine's name comes from the four strokes taken by a piston inside a cylinder in the engine. The first stroke of the cycle is called the *intake* stroke. It takes place when a mixture of gasoline and air reaches the cylinder and the piston sucks the mixture into it through a valve opening. The second stroke is called the *compression* stroke. The valve closes and the piston goes up, squeezing (or compressing) the mixture. The third stroke is called the

power stroke. When the piston reaches the top of the cylinder, a spark plug makes an electric spark which explodes the mixture, and forces the piston down again. The fourth stroke is called the *exhaust* stroke. Another valve now opens and as the piston comes up again it forces the burnt mixture of air and gas out of the cylinder. And as the piston comes down after the exhaust stroke, it brings in a fresh mixture of gasoline and air to start the four parts of the cycle again: intake, compression, power, and exhaust.

All of this happens so swiftly, of course, that the series of explosions sound like one steady roar. When four or more cylinders are in the engine, as is the case with most present-day automobiles, this series of explosions provides steady power to make a car go smoothly and efficiently over miles of mountain roads and desert highways.

Buick 1908

hand crank

A hand crank was used in early automobiles to start the engine running.

Stop and Go

An engine alone will not operate a car. Before Otto's engine could be used in a vehicle, a number of problems had to be solved: how to start the engine, how to keep fuel coming to it, how to keep the engine from overheating, how to keep a steady engine speed while turning wheels whose speed varied, and how to stop the car.

The early automobile men found answers to most of these problems, al-though many of their results did not survive the first experimental cars. Sometimes the ideas were as crude as Otto's first engine itself, but were so basically sound that, except for im-provements in design and efficiency, they have not changed today.

THE STARTER.

To bring the early automobile en-gine to the point where it would con-

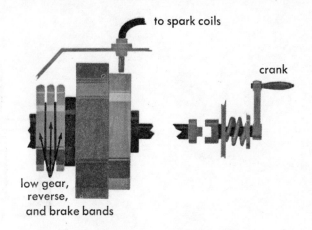

to spark coils

crank

low gear, reverse, and brake bands

The hand crank was wound until the spark ignited the fuel, thus moving the pistons.

tinue its four cycles of operation under its own power required great physical strength. The engine had to be cranked by hand until the spark ignited the fuel mixture and sent the pistons on their up and down motion. Cranking was not easy, especially in the fall and winter when the engine was cold. Sometimes the hand crank would snap back after the engine started and would seriously injure the motorist. Many devices were made to prevent such accidents, but none were reliable until the electric self-starter was invented. This was a small electric motor which was operated by a storage battery. This motor had enough power to start the engine. Once the engine started, the motor disconnected itself; its job was done. The self-starter took the hard work—and much of the fear—out of operating an automobile. Many automobile experts consider it the single greatest improvement in automobiles since their inception.

The first American self-starter was invented by Rushmore and was available (at extra cost) in 1911 on several cars such as the Simplex.

Cadillac, in 1912, was the first car to install an electric self-starter as regular equipment. However this particular starter, invented by Charles Kettering, was never as successful as Rushmore's, which all cars still use today.

The electric self-starting motor, still used today, took the hard work out of operating a car.

SECTIONAL VIEW OF STARTING MOTOR

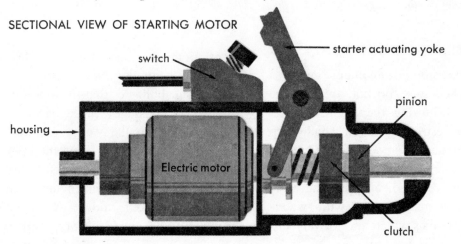

switch

starter actuating yoke

pinion

housing

Electric motor

clutch

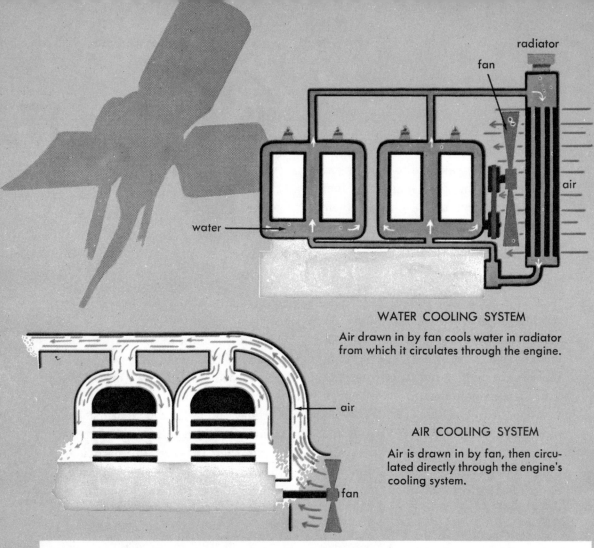

WATER COOLING SYSTEM

Air drawn in by fan cools water in radiator from which it circulates through the engine.

AIR COOLING SYSTEM

Air is drawn in by fan, then circulated directly through the engine's cooling system.

Air or water cooling systems are used to dispel the heat generated by the automobile engine.

COOLING AND OILING SYSTEMS.

The operation of an engine develops heat. When it is too hot, there is the danger of hurting the engine's metal parts, or destroying the oil which keep the parts running smoothly. For highest efficiency, much of the engine's heat should be reduced, and this the early automobile makers did with water-cooling systems which are not very dif-ferent from the ones we use today. From the beginning, the automobile engine was built so that it was sur-rounded by passages through which water could circulate and radiators were to be found in all but the very earliest and most primitive cars. Other makers tried to cool their engines with air. This worked quite well; but throughout the auto's history, only a few air-cooled cars have been available, one being the Volkswagen. Air cooling has been most successful in airplanes where the propellers throw the air directly to the cooling system.

To keep the moving metal parts of an engine running without friction requires lubrication. This means that they must be bathed in oil or grease at all times. In early cars this was solved by putting oil in the crankcase beneath the engine where a connecting rod would dip into it as the engine turned. The motion of the rod would cause the oil to splash and, it was hoped, lubricate all parts of the engine. This system worked quite well on the early low-speed engines, but in our present-day higher-speed models, oil is fed to the engine by a pressure system; other moving parts of the car are packed with grease at regular intervals.

Engines must be oiled constantly to prevent friction between the moving metal parts.

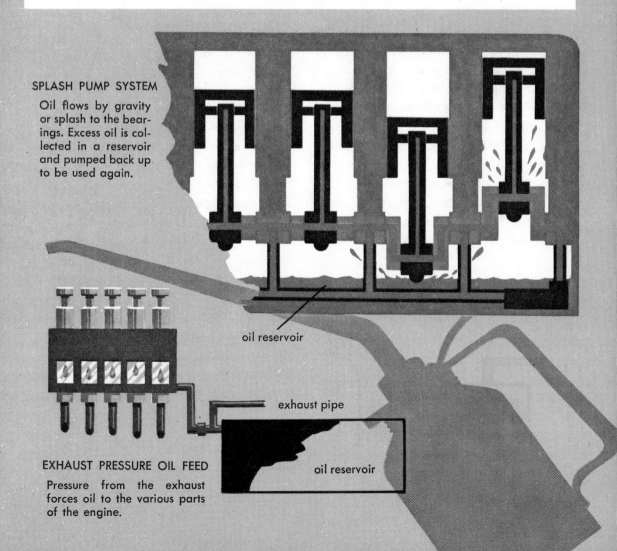

SPLASH PUMP SYSTEM
Oil flows by gravity or splash to the bearings. Excess oil is collected in a reservoir and pumped back up to be used again.

oil reservoir

exhaust pipe

EXHAUST PRESSURE OIL FEED
Pressure from the exhaust forces oil to the various parts of the engine.

oil reservoir

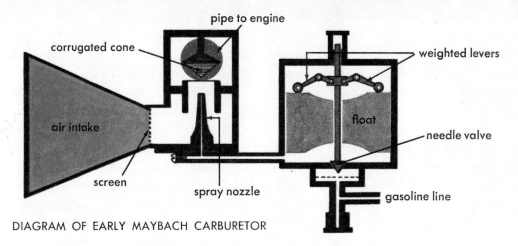

DIAGRAM OF EARLY MAYBACH CARBURETOR

The float controls the mixture of gas and air which flows into the carburetor.

CARBURETION.

For an engine to operate efficiently, there must be a proper mixture of fuel and air. The part of the engine which mixes the two is called the carburetor. The first of the kind still used today, the float-feed carburetor, was patented by William Maybach in 1893. However, in early cars the mixing was done in several other ways, too.

Hiram P. Maxim, one of the automobile pioneers, used a simple carbu-

PRINCIPLE OF
SIMPLE FLOAT
FEED CARBURETOR

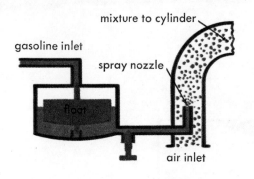

retor in his first car. It was a gasoline-soaked rag from which the fuel fell into the engine a drop at a time. Some car builders used a wick carburetor in which a woolen cloth was looped on a series of rods. One end of the cloth was in the gas tank, the other at the cylinder head. The fuel traveled along the cloth, vaporizing as it came, so that by the time it reached the engine it would be ready to explode.

Some of the first cars had mixing devices of the float-feed variety which consisted of a needle valve which permitted the gasoline to flow to a chamber where it combined with air before being carried to the engine. The driver could control the flow of gasoline into the chamber by a hand device on the steering wheel.

But finally the float-feed carburetor, the type used in today's cars, came into use and replaced all the others. The first successful one was used on Maxim's Mark V Columbia in 1898.

TRANSMISSION.

The system of carrying the engine's power to the wheels which make the car go is known as the transmission. Today we take for granted the automatic nature of this job, whether by pushbuttons or by a simple lever on the steering column. Yet it was one of the most difficult problems for early automobile makers to solve; and over the years, the transmission has been one of the most intensively studied parts of a car.

To begin with, an automobile engine runs at a higher speed than the wheels. It is important to be able to control the speed at which the engine turns the car's wheels because even on the shortest rides no car ever maintains constant speed. To get up steep hills or out of snow or mud, needs force from the engine—but not much speed. When we are rolling at a steady pace on a superhighway we want the engine to turn more slowly in order to save gasoline. We want our cars to back up as well as go forward. And when we stop for a traffic light we want the engine to keep turning while the car is at a standstill. The transmission permits us to do all these things by the use of gears of various sizes. They control the speed with which the car's wheels turn. One gear, called reverse, causes the car to move backward. When the gears are disengaged, the car will not move no matter how fast the engine turns.

Not all early transmissions were capable of doing these jobs. The most popular transmission on the first cars was called a planetary transmission. It got its name because when looked at from the end, its one large gear with a series of small gears revolving around, it looked like a model of the sun and the planets. By shifting the proper lever a driver could change from low to high engine speed, or shift into reverse. The greatest advantage of this type of transmission was that the gears could not be stripped when shifting because they were always in contact with each other. Around 1900, the French developed a sliding gear transmission whereby as many as four different forward speeds were possible. Many of the expensive early American cars used it, but low priced cars had a planetary transmission—noisy and inefficient—throughout the early years.

At whatever speed they turn, the gears connect with a long rod which runs under the car to the rear axle. This is called the propeller shaft. At right angles from its end extends the rear axle which attaches to the rear wheels. In modern cars, the propeller shaft's turning causes gears in the axle housing to turn the wheels. Not so in the early cars. Following the pattern of the bicycle, early automobile makers connected a chain on sprockets directly from the transmission to the rear axle. Some of the more expensive cars used double chains, one connected to each of the rear wheels. They were noisy and

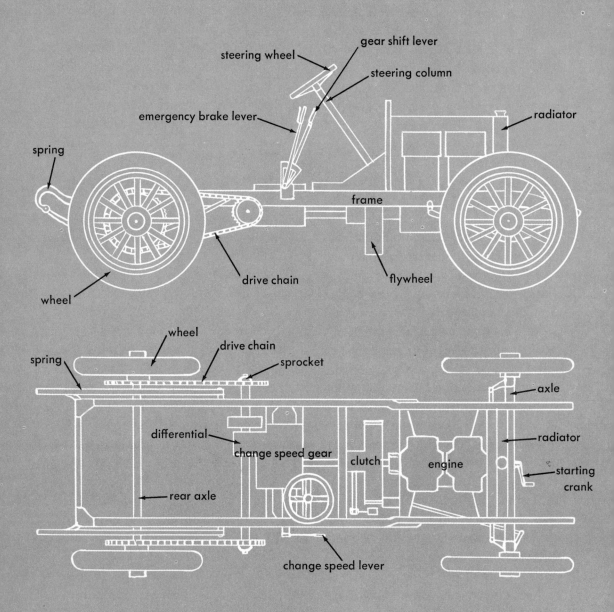

steering wheel

gear shift lever

steering column

radiator

emergency brake lever

spring

frame

drive chain

flywheel

wheel

wheel

drive chain

sprocket

spring

axle

differential

radiator

change speed gear

clutch

engine

starting crank

rear axle

change speed lever

A DOUBLE CHAIN DRIVEN CAR

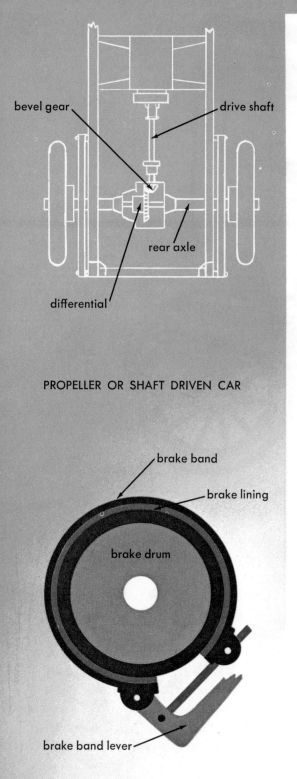

bevel gear

drive shaft

rear axle

differential

PROPELLER OR SHAFT DRIVEN CAR

brake band

brake lining

brake drum

brake band lever

dirty, and broke with annoying frequency. Even when a rear axle similar to those in use today was developed, many manufacturers insisted on keeping the open chain drive. Some trucks specializing in very heavy work still use the chain system to good effect.

BRAKES.

Being able to make a car stop is often more important than making it go. The earliest brakes were often hand or foot levers which caused a band of metal to move against the brake drum. There, friction would cause it to slow down and, sooner or later, stop. Since few of the early cars were capable of great speed, braking was not considered as important as it is today. In time, brakes were fitted to the rear wheels where foot pressure applied to a floor pedal caused a drum-like surface to be brought against a circular band in the rear wheels. The resulting friction forced the wheels to stop turning. Four-wheel brakes did not come into widespread use until the 1920's, and soon after they were standard on most American cars. With the increased speeds and work loads of today's cars and trucks, the *hydraulic brake,* a glycerine compound in cylinders, and the *compressed-air brake,* air in cylinders, are improvements upon the original *mechanical brake.*

Early brakes were operated by a hand or foot lever which caused a band of metal to push against the brake drum.

Like the horse-drawn surreys they replaced, some early cars had fringed canopies.

MOTOR CAR OR HORSELESS CARRIAGE.

The logical place to put engines on the first cars seemed to be beneath the floorboard of the carriage. There was no obstruction of vision. The resulting vehicles were indeed carriages without horses. After all, they were designed to be horse-drawn. This influence was so strong, in fact, that many of the early American cars carried a whip socket, although few owners used it to hold actual whips.

Before 1900, the Daimler Company in Germany put the engine in front of the carriage in a space designed especially to hold it. Americans call this space the hood; the British call it the bonnet. Under any name, this move took automobile design away from that resembling horse carriages and led the way to the appearance of cars as we know them today.

With the engine up front, body designers worked to make the car more

20

comfortable for drivers and passengers. Many early cars had no tops for protection against the weather, but were an optional feature, just as they had been on buggies. Nor were there doors to the front seats. Sometimes a rear door was available for back seat passengers. By 1905 there were side doors already shown the advantage of rubber tires filled with air. By 1900, nearly all cars were using bicycle type tires. They did not have tubes and were almost impossible to repair. By 1905, tubes and tire casing were separate, but not until demountable rims came into general use around 1915 was tire

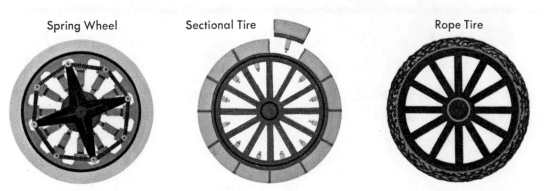

Spring Wheel   Sectional Tire   Rope Tire

Early tires were made of solid rubber, wire, or rope. Pneumatic tires came into use by 1900.

—but to the passenger compartment only. In 1911 front doors came in, and soon some daring manufacturers — among them Ford and Cadillac—were offering closed bodies as standard features. But it was not until the 'teens that closed bodies were generally available.

RIDING ON AIR.

Since the horse-drawn carriage was the only model for engine-powered cars to follow, many of its features were taken over without change. The first cars rolled on high, wooden-spoked wheels, although wire wheels had become more popular. But bicycles had

changing made relatively easy. This permitted the tire to be removed from the wheel, to be repaired later while the car proceeded on a spare tire. Tedious hours of getting a tire off the wheel, repairing it, pumping it by the side of the road, and then replacing it were no longer necessary.

Early tires were usually made of canvas covered by rubber and rarely gave more than 1,000 miles of use. By 1920, tougher cord had replaced the fabric. A few years later, balloon tires, requiring less air pressure than the old tires, brought greater comfort and safety to travelers.

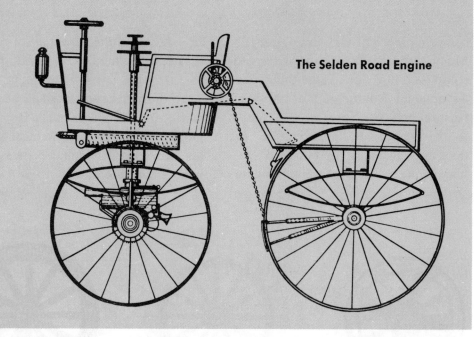

George B. Selden patented this two-cycle internal combustion road engine in 1895.

Selden and his Magic patent

Fireworks exploded and the streets were gay with merrymakers in Philadelphia during the summer of 1876. America was celebrating the 100th anniversary of its independence. And Philadelphia was providing the biggest show of all—the Centennial Exposition. On exhibit were models and displays of American progress in the arts and in science. One of the most popular exhibits was a new type of two cycle internal-combustion engine shown by George B. Brayton. There was no compression of the gases in the combustion cylinder. This was done in a pump cylinder with the gases igniting as they traveled from this cylinder to the other. Of those who watched it work, none was more interested than a patent attorney from Rochester, New York, named George B. Selden.

Selden saw at once the potential of an engine run by liquid fuel. He was sure it could move a road vehicle. After the exposition he read everything he could find about these engines, especially reports concerning the numerous experiments in continental Europe. In 1879, Selden applied for a patent on an automobile to be powered by an internal-combustion engine patterned on the Brayton cycle engine.

In Germany in 1885, Gottlieb Daimler and Karl Benz, working independently, had used gasoline in Otto's four cycle engine and had made it propel a car. These two men are the true "inventors" of the automobile, for they were the first to continue developing their ideas until they had a really workable automobile model. Emile Levassor and René Panhard started making cars in the 1890's. They used Daimler's engine which they put in the front of the machine, an innovation. Soon, French and German cars were being built on their plans. But there was no immediate rush to build cars in this country. Selden seemed to sense the great future of automobiles, however, and knew that if he were to profit from his patent he had to keep it alive until cars were actually being produced. For sixteen years he made changes in his design which kept the patent from being issued until 1895. This meant that he could collect royalties from any manufacturer making cars based upon design for the next seventeen years.

Selden assigned the patent to the Electric Vehicle Company in 1899 which proceeded to charge every U.S. automobile maker 1¼ per cent of the retail price of the cars they built. By that time, men in various parts of the country were beginning to roll out experimental cars in back alleys, on farm roads and on city streets. It looked as if Selden was on his way to becoming a rich man by inventing a car which he had not built or run. But Selden made one major mistake. His patent was for a Brayton cycle engine, and nearly all American gasoline driven cars were based on Otto's four cycle engine. Many automobile manufacturers did not pay royalties to Selden. The test case came in 1903, when Henry Ford refused to pay the fee for the cars he was making. He was sued. After two trials, the courts decided in 1911 that the Selden patent did not cover a car using a four cycle engine. Manufacturers no longer had to pay royalties to Selden. Now cars could be built without fear of a lawsuit.

The Association of Licensed Automobile Manufacturers was formed in 1903 to give Selden patent licenses.

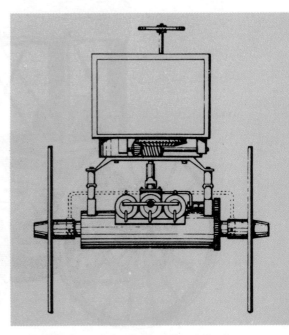

Front view of the Selden Road Engine.

First on the Road

The inventors of the first gasoline-powered automobile to run in the United States were the Duryea brothers who were raised on a farm in Illinois. But their interest was mechanics, not farming. At 17, Charles built a bicycle using only a magazine picture as a guide. The brothers came east, Charles to work in a bicycle factory, Frank as a toolmaker. In 1891 they read about the gasoline engines being built in Europe, and of the horseless carriages they propelled. The Duryeas decided to build one of their own.

It took them a year to reach the trial stage, but during the summer of 1893 they had a car which could go. It did not move much faster than most of us walk, but it moved. It had a four horse-power, one cylinder, four cycle engine and weighed 750 pounds. It may be seen today in the Smithsonian Institution in Washington, with an improved engine and transmission which the

The four horsepower 1892-93 Duryea may be seen in Washington's Smithsonian Institution.

Duryea 1892-93

Duryeas later installed. A year later, the Duryea car with improvements traveled ten miles an hour. By 1896, ten Duryeas were manufactured and sold. That year their first advertisement appeared, claiming that the "new models are the finest specimen of the carriage maker's art ever produced for motor vehicles." And that year, the Duryea car was on display in Barnum and Bailey's Circus where it could be seen "Every Day in the New Street Parade."

The first Duryea had its engine under the body of the buggy, with its cylinder above the rear axle. The power from the engine turned a set of gears which connected with another set on a jackshaft. On this were sprockets which connected, by chain, to larger sprockets on the inside of the rear wheel. The Duryea had a primitive transmission which was operated by moving the steering tiller up and down. This provided two forward speeds, high and low. There was one reverse speed. Engine speed was controlled by a needle valve which determined the flow of gasoline to the engine. A crank in the rear started the car. It rolled on high wheels with iron bands—noisily, uncomfortably, slowly, but definitely, into American automobile history.

THE CAR FROM KOKOMO

Elwood Haynes of Kokomo, Indiana, was a field superintendent for the Indiana Natural Gas and Oil Company

Rear View of Duryea

In the early Duryea, tanks over the rear axle carried water and gasoline.

in 1892. This meant that he spent nearly every day riding rough or muddy roads in a horse and buggy. After months of this kind of travel he decided that there had to be a better way to get around. Haynes had studied engineering and chemistry, and had taught school before he took a job with the gas company. He read the scientific journals regularly. The progress being reported abroad in gasoline engines excited him, and he decided to build a motor-driven vehicle of his own.

Haynes was not a mechanic, so he turned to Elmer Apperson who ran a machine shop in Kokomo. Elmer, and his brother Edgar, who repaired bicycles, liked Haynes' plans. From the fall of 1893 to the summer of 1894 they drew designs, tinkered, and finally built. On the Fourth of July, 1894, they were ready for their first test.

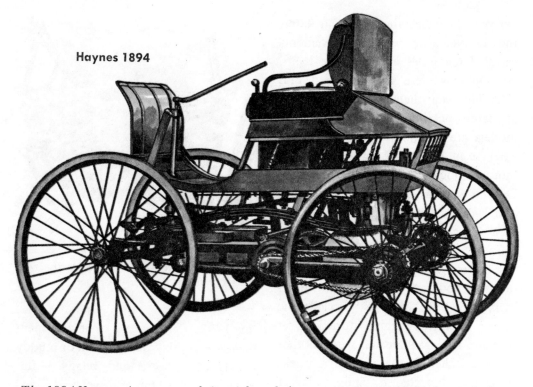

Haynes 1894

The 1894 Haynes-Apperson made its trial run before a curious crowd in Kokomo, Indiana.

Haynes and the Apperson brothers hired a horse to pull their vehicle out of town. With a curious holiday crowd watching, Elmer Apperson cranked the engine while Elwood Haynes sat at the tiller. To the amazement of the crowd the engine started. Apperson hopped aboard and the strange vehicle rolled back to Kokomo without stalling.

The Haynes-Apperson car was powered by a one horsepower, two cycle engine which turned gears attached to the same kind of sprockets and chain used by the Duryea car. However, the two cars differed in many respects. The Haynes-Apperson tiller did nothing but steer. A separate vertical rod permitted the driver to shift from high to low and back again. There was no reverse. The car had to be turned around by pushing and pulling if there was no room on the road for it to make a complete turn by itself. But it did have a foot accelerator on the floorboard to increase and decrease engine speed, a seemingly optimistic extra. The experiment proved a great success and led to later development and improvement of the Haynes-Apperson design.

A 1907 newspaper advertised the Apperson "Jack Rabbit" for "racing or touring."

26

The APPERSON JACK RABBIT

Guaranteed Speed 75 miles per hour

Only 15 cars of this type will be built for 1907

IN presenting "THE JACK RABBIT" we are catering to
that limited class of owners who want a car that can be
put to any service—racing or touring. The car is almost a
duplicate of our Vanderbilt Racing Car, and built on the following

Specifications—50-60 horse-power. Weight 1,800 to 1,900 pounds. Wheel base,
100 inches. Tread, 56 inches. Wheels, 34 front and rear. Tires, 34x3½ front;
34x4 rear. Quick detachable rims. Bearings, Hess-Bright. Double Ignition System,
using magneto and coil. Four-speed, selective type transmission. Tank capacity,
20 gallons. Axles, I-beam, Krupp nickel steel. Clearance, 9½ inches. Gear ratio,
1 7-11 to 1. Construction, Krupp nickel steel throughout.

Price $5,000.00

APPERSON BROS. AUTOMOBILE CO.
M. A. L. A. M.
KOKOMO, INDIANA

BRANCHES
1665 Broadway, Cor. 52d & Broad'y, N.Y. 8 Columbus Ave., Boston
338 N. Broad Street, Philadelphia 1240 Michigan Ave., Chicago

The Great Chicago Race

Soon after automobiles began to move under their own power, it seemed quite logical that there should be a race to see which one could move the fastest. Men had raced horses and bicycles. Why not cars? The first automobile race in the world was held in France, and was run from Paris to Rouen, a

distance of about 80 miles. It took place on July 22, 1894. Of the 21 starters, 17 finished the race; the winner, in 6 hours and 48 minutes; the last car, in 13 hours.

News of the French race excited car builders in America. It also brought about the first American car race,

The Duryea and the Benz took an early lead in the Great Chicago Race, Thanksgiving, 1895.

sponsored by H. H. Kohlsaat, publisher of the Chicago Times-Herald. In July, he announced the offer of a purse of $5,000 of which the winner would get $2,000. Immediately there was a rush of applications, mostly by people who had not yet built a car. The race was originally scheduled for November 2, 1895, but it became obvious as that date approached that few, if any, of the

entries would be ready. The date was finally set for Thanksgiving Day.

To keep up interest in the race during the postponement, the Times-Herald started a second contest to find a name for the new vehicles. It was to replace "horseless carriage" which was what automobiles were still being called. The winning name was "Motocycle." The newspaper prophesied that the word would "come into general use" since it was "more expressive than 'automobile,' 'vehicle motor,' or any phrase that has been suggested." Soon after, a magazine called "The Moto-cycle" started publication. Neither the name nor the magazine lasted any length of time.

On Thanksgiving Day, 1895, Chicago was covered with deep snow and slush. Shortly before 9:00 a.m. there were only six cars at the starting line in Jackson Park. A Haynes-Apperson was badly damaged on the way to the park. Other builders did not complete their vehicles in time. Of the starters two were electrically driven. The other four were gasoline powered, of which three were models of the German Benz, entered by American distributors, and one was American, the Duryea. The race was to the suburb of Evanston and back, a distance of 54 miles.

At 8:55 the first car moved off and the race had started. Each car carried a driver, a mechanic, and an umpire. The Duryea was the first to get away, but it broke down while still in the city and was passed by a Benz entered by the R. H. Macy department store of New York. But Frank Duryea, who was driving the car which he and his brother built for the race, made his repairs quickly and set out after the Macy Benz. He was forty minutes behind the German car at Lincoln Park, but by the half-way point at Evanston, his car was able to pass the Benz.

Due to snow, the distance of the race had been reduced, but, nevertheless, on the return half, Duryea lost his way in the snow and went two miles off course. When he found his way back he was still in the lead. The Macy Benz which had started so gloriously collided with a horse-drawn hack outside of Evanston and was forced to quit the race. At 7:18 p.m. Duryea crossed the finish line—the first winner of America's first automobile race. He had covered the 54 miles in ten hours and 23 minutes.

The only other car to finish was the Benz entered by the H. Mueller Manufacturing Company. It had overcome motor, clutch, and sprocket troubles. Its starting driver had passed out from exposure to the cold. Despite this, it came in an hour and a half behind the Duryea. The two electric cars reached the half-way point, came back part way, but did not finish.

The Chicago Race intensified American interest in automobiles, and especially in those powered by gasoline engines. It gave great impetus to the mechanics, inventors and tinkerers who had been working in barns and cellars away from those people who scoffed and proclaimed the virtues of the horse. After the race, more and more people conceded that the automobile had a future. Soon, new cars would be seen on the roads by the dozens, then the hundreds, and finally by the hundreds of thousands.

Packard Roadster 1901

THE
Horseless Age

VOLUME 14

JULY 13, 1904

NUMBER 2

WINTON

Most Motor Cars Are Safe

ordinarily, but in severest tests—such as any motorist may encounter unexpectedly—extreme strength of construction and a powerful motor are absolutely indispensable. The possession of these features—the WINTON Factor of Safety—gives the owner a sense of security that other motorists don't have.

Complete with canopy top, lamps . . . .

THE

BRANCH HOUS

WINTON IS KING
It wears the crown of excellence

Reo Runabout 1906

The Rise and Fall of the Electric Car

Despite the success of gasoline-powered cars in races in Europe and the United States, there were still a great many people who were convinced that electricity was the best means to move a vehicle. Electric cars could run in complete silence, while gasoline engines made a great racket. Electric cars were clean while gasoline engines and other parts of the car were oily and greasy. Electric cars were simple enough for a child to operate. A simple lever did everything. No cranking, no carburetor difficulties, no oil or gas to worry about.

Electric cars had one major disadvantage, and this proved their downfall. They could run only as long as there was a charge in the storage batteries—and the charges did not last long. The early electrics had a range of from 25 to 40 miles, with a top speed of 15 miles per hour. Just before World War I, when electric cars were at the peak of their popularity, the driving range had been increased to about 100 miles, and some of them could go as fast as 25 miles per hour.

The power plant of the electric car was the least complicated of any early automobile. It consisted of a number of storage batteries linked together. The batteries were connected to a driving motor in front of the rear axle. The controller switch made changes of speed direction extremely simple. Ease of operation made it especially popular with women, who rarely sought high speed. And if they limited their driving to social calls in the city, they were really not very concerned with the car's limited driving range. Some makers of electric cars cultivated the women's trade by putting solid rubber tires on the wheels. This meant that in addition to its other advantages for them, women were also free of the worry of flat tires or blowouts.

Since the power plant was no problem to install, the builders of electric cars devoted most of their attention to the bodies. As a result, some of the electrics had considerably more style and elegance than other early cars. Some were patterned after the handsomest horse carriages which had the chauffeur sitting high on the back, steering with a tiller bar, while his passengers sat daintily up front. Later, when more and more closed models were offered, buyers were given a wide choice of upholstery, window curtains and flower vases. One electric, built especially for the King of Siam in 1909, had a body finished in ivory, a leather top, patent leather fenders, all metal parts silver-plated and the tiller handle made of pearl.

Although electrics found their greatest favor with women, they were also

**Columbia
Electric 1900**

Argo Electric Chassis

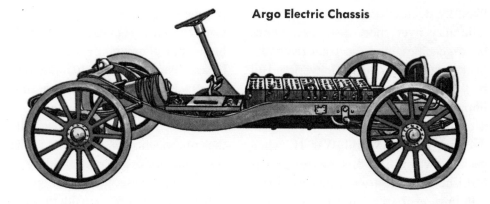

Electric Motor

*The rise of the electric car was due not only to the
ease and convenience with which it was handled,
but also to its cleanliness and beauty. However,
these cars could run only so long as their storage
batteries held out, generally for about 100 miles.*

The 1905 Columbia Electric Brougham was enclosed for passenger comfort.

liked by doctors because of their quiet reliability over short distances. Shops in large cities used electric-driven delivery wagons tor local deliveries. But by 1914, gasoline engine cars were so improved that the electrics went into a decline and then finally out of production. During World War II, when gasoline was rationed, some people refurbished old electrics which were still standing in barns and garages, and rode quietly about their business. Today, these mementos of a slower, quieter, more genteel period in the history of the American automobile may be seen only in museums.

There has been a current revival of interest in the United States in the use of electric cars. Faced with mounting problems of auto traffic and air pollution caused by exhaust, the nation's municipal planners are considering the ideas advanced by such industrial designers as Raymond Loewy, promoting serious consideration of the intra-city use of electric cars. Difficulties still face the proponents of such plans. However, the necessity of providing some solution to these municipal problems will require careful consideration.

34

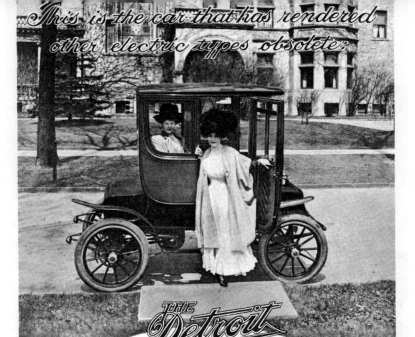

This is the car that has rendered other electric types obsolete.

The Detroit Electric "Mayor's Coach" appealed particularly to ladies because of its elegance and ease in handling.

THE Detroit ELECTRIC

Let us recapitulate briefly some of the points which have won first place for the Detroit Electric, almost by common consent.

Here in Detroit—the automobile center of America—the Detroit has displaced all other models.

Here, and in every community of consequence, it is the chosen car of the electrical engineer, the builder of gas cars—the men of technical and practical experience.

How has this come to pass?

The picture practically answers this question.

It shows a car of surpassing elegance and dignity.

It shows that the Detroit door opens to the front instead of the rear—

The step pads are oval instead of having sharp square corners—

The cushions are more luxurious; the rear one 20 inches deep; the front one 15 inches. The deepest you have ever seen in a electric are 18 and 19, 13 and 14 inches—

The curved front windows are larger; there is nothing what ever to obscure the operator's vision at any angle—

The grab handles on the doors—and all trimming —are silver finished.

So much—although these are only the more im portant points—that makes for perfect ease an luxury in the Detroit.

Let us look over the mechanical and operating details.

The battery is larger and more powerful.

You get more mileage and greater speed— many a Detroit owner, in continuous every-day service, is getting a consistent average of 85 miles ; and 100 miles is easily possible.

You have five speeds forward and one reverse. You had thought three forward and one reverse the ultimate limit.

Speed control, the alarm and motor brake are concentrated in one lever—simplest and easiest control.

Mounting the motor under the body in the center of the frame removes undue weight and strain from the rear axle and tires.

We could go on enumerating full fifty distinctive Detroit features, improvements which make for efficiency and econ-

Anderson Ca
Dept. B,

A 1910 Royal Daimler limousine was built as a gift for George V, King of England.

A specially designed and lavishly equipped car was built for the Rajah of Dewas in 1911.

35

The Steam Car

Even after the success of the internal-combustion engine, men did not give up on steam power as a means of propelling an automobile. By the 1890's these experimenters had come a long way from Cugnot's vehicle of 1769. They did so well, in fact, that by the turn of the century steam cars outnumbered gasoline cars in many parts of the country. The steam car builders had overcome many of the problems which baffled Cugnot and his successors for a period of more than a hundred years.

Steam cars were fast and quiet. There were no gears to shift. People worried from time to time that the boiler of a steam car would explode, but none ever did. The mechanics of a steam car were simplicity itself.

A steel boiler was heated by a kerosene burner which in turn was kept

Steam power, quieter and less complicated than gasoline engines, continued to be used to propel road vehicles. On the opposite page is the Roper steam velocipede, built about 1869; to its right is an early model of the Stanley Steamer. Above, in a steam velocipede made in France, the passenger rode in front of the driver.

The 1897 Stanley Steamer, designed by the Stanley brothers, was first tested amid much confusion in the quiet Massachusetts community of Newton.

burning by a pilot burner using gasoline. Even when the pilot was kept burning all the time, a gallon of gasoline would last all day. The main burner itself gave about ten miles to a gallon. The boiler turned the water into steam which drove a two cylinder engine. This operated directly on the driving gear. A lever on the steering wheel controlled the car's speed. It was pulled up slowly to start, up further for more speed or on hills, and down to slow the car. A brake pedal stopped it. A reverse pedal caused the lever to make the car go backward—as swiftly as it could go forward.

There were drawbacks, of course. They would run only on white gasoline. To bring the steam pressure up to the point where it could operate the engine often meant waiting a half hour or more after the main burner was lighted. A steamer with a storage type boiler often kept the pilot lit all the time so it could be used a few minutes after the main burner was turned on. A flash boiler steamer only took a few minutes to get going. Burners and boilers had to be cleaned often—a messy job. On the road, the driver had to watch his pressure and water-level gauges constantly. In the early models, there had to be water stops every 25 miles or so. Later, condensers were used which converted the steam back to water so it could be used over again, thus permitting one filling of water to last 200 miles.

Some steamers were still being made in the 1920's. But by then gasoline powered automobiles were cheap. Steamers were not produced on assembly lines, and as a result were expensive. They went out of favor with the public. But there are automotive designers today who think that with the application of modern technology, steam powered automobiles could be built which would outperform most modern gasoline powered cars.

THE FASTEST THING ON WHEELS

Francis E. and Frelan O. Stanley were identical twins right down to the trim of their long flowing beards. Their interests were also identical. Together they had invented a photographic dry plate which they sold to the Eastman Kodak Company. Together in 1896 they saw their first automobile at the county fair at Brockton, Massachusetts.

The car the Stanley brothers saw was a steamer, but so badly made it could not go a half mile without having to stop to build up steam pressure. The Stanleys were sure they could build a better car, although at the time, they knew almost nothing about steam engines.

Despite their lack of knowledge, the Stanleys bought the rights to a set of blueprints late in 1896 and set about ordering the parts to assemble a car. After some months, they were finished. After spending nearly a year in designing and redesigning the engine and

boiler, the ingenious Stanley twins finally assembled a light, two-seater runabout. On a clear September day in 1897, they built up a head of steam, watched the gauge for a few minutes, and decided the time had come for a road test.

With Francis E. at the tiller (steering wheels came later) and Frelan O. as passenger, the first Stanley Steamer moved out of a back alley onto a major thoroughfare. At once, as the shrill whistle of the steam car pierced the normal quiet of Newton, Massachusetts, the first damage was done. A horse hitched to a produce wagon turned toward the source of the strange sound. What it saw was so frightening that it gave one snort and jumped,

The famous 1912 Stanley Steamer was referred to as "the fastest thing on wheels."

Stanley Steamer 1912

The engine of the Stanley Steamer that made a world speed record in 1906, racing 127 mph.

breaking the traces of the wagon. The startled horse did not stop running until it reached Newtonville Square, four miles away. The trial run was not an auspicious one.

The runaway horse did not disturb the Stanleys as much as the size of their engine. They needed one of much less weight to power the kind of light car they wanted to build. Following the Stanleys' own design a local machine shop produced an engine that weighed 32½ pounds, with the boiler. And other parts made the total weight of the power plant 150 pounds. The Stanleys built two cars and this was as far as they intended to go. It had never occurred to them to build cars for sale.

But when people saw the Stanley Steamer they wanted to buy one like it. Then, after a remarkable exhibition of the Steamer's ability at Boston's first automobile show, the demand became too great for the Stanleys to resist. Reluctantly, the Stanleys had allowed their car to be entered in a speed contest connected with this show and held at the Charles River Trotting Track, November 8, 1898. It won in the record time of 2 minutes 11 seconds for a mile. Then they entered the car in a hill-climbing contest. All the other contestants dropped out as the Stanley whizzed its way to the top of a steep grade. Within two weeks of these achievements, more than 200 requests for cars had reached the Stanleys. Finally, they decided to enter the automobile business.

For a number of years to come, many Americans were to believe that steam power was the most efficient way to move a car. Of all the steam-powered cars then available, none attained the fame and glory of the Stanley Steamer — in its prime, the fastest thing on wheels.

Eventually, gas engines replaced steam-powered ones. Many people were uneasy about riding in a car with a boiler of live steam. It took a long time to build up steam pressure, and there were frequent troubles with the boilers.

Winton 1903

The 1903 Winton two-seater was the epitome of speed and beauty in its day.

Early Favorites, and Some That Lasted

In the history of the American automobile, about 2,200 different makes of cars have appeared. Most of them made a brief debut in the early years of automobile development, and then faded from view. Only a handful of the pioneer cars have survived.

Many makers lacked the money to maintain production. Some turned out inferior products which did not sell at all. A few, which are no longer in existence, helped make automotive history. They shined brightly, and then departed — victims of faulty business methods, of mass-produced cheap cars,

the Depression, and changing American taste. No longer with us are some old-time favorites—the air-cooled Franklin, the Pierce-Arrow whose headlights extended from the front fenders, and the Packard which once stood as the most desirable car in the land.

One car, which in its day represented the ultimate in speed and beauty, was the Winton. It was built by Alexander Winton, one of the auto pioneers who had faith in the car's future. He built his first model in 1896, and two more in 1897, and, what is more, he built to sell. The first sale was on March 24th, 1898. To make the public conscious of his car, he undertook a number of stunts to promote it. In July-August 1897 he drove a Winton from Cleveland, Ohio, to New York City, a distance of 800 miles over poor or non-existent roads, in just ten days. It was quite an achievement and the publicity received by the Winton car assured its popularity for years to come. Winton entered every race and hill climbing contest he could find. For a while he won nearly all of them. In early 1902, a young automobile maker named Henry Ford built a car he called "999" for the express purpose of beating the Winton. Ford conquered Winton's best car on October 25th, 1902. The victory established the Ford as a serious rival and was the beginning of a permanent decline for the Winton.

A car which goes back to the earliest days of the American automobile and is still in production is the Oldsmobile. It was named for Ransom E. Olds, who experimented with steam and electric cars before he made gasoline powered cars. In 1897, Olds developed a car with a one-cylinder

The 1905 Franklin had a carriage top which provided partial shelter during bad weather.

Franklin 1905

Curved Dash Oldsmobile 1902

The 1902 Curved Dash Oldsmobile, designed to sell for $650, was a sporty and highly popular model which was to give rise to the song, "In My Merry Oldsmobile."

The car would be driven from Detroit to New York in time for the 1901 Automobile Show.

The car made it. Its endurance record and its good looks, in contrast to the heavy vehicles of the day, brought the Oldsmobile immediate popularity. It is said that orders were taken for 1,000 cars during the show, an unheard of number at that time. The Olds company was saved. And the stylish little car became the best seller of its day. Automobile makers learned then that body design was an important factor in selling cars.

In 1905, the car was immortalized in a song called "In My Merry Oldsmobile," published by the country's leading music firm, M. Witmark and Sons. It was one of the first of about 600 songs which have been inspired by the automobile over the years, and has remained the best known.

With the rapid technological advance of the automobile in the past sixty years, antique models of early manufacturing ventures (such as the Oldsmobile) have become extremely valuable. While many early cars are still in private hands, there are a goodly number exhibited in museums throughout the country. The Smithsonian Institution in Washington, D.C. houses an outstanding American collection.

gasoline engine which was successful enough to bring financial support to start a company. But before production could get started, a fire in March 1901 destroyed the Olds factory. The only thing saved was a small car with a curved dashboard which gave it a youthful, jaunty appearance. Olds had designed it to sell for $650, one of a number of models he planned to bring out that year. There was no money to rebuild the factory, but there was enough for a do-or-die publicity stunt.

Primitive road conditions often led to abandoned cars and ruffled tempers.

How to Get From Here to There

In the early years of the automobile, driving was a hazardous affair in the United States. Except for certain city streets, America's roads were dirt paths. They were dusty in the summer, muddy after rain, and always pitted with holes which could break an axle, or covered with sharp stones which could puncture a tire. A motorist who made 50 miles in one day was considered a daring adventurer. This was rarely done without a maddening assortment of breakdowns.

Agitation for better roads had started in the 1880's by bicyclists who had discovered the pleasures of touring the countryside. But very little progress had been made by the time automobiles came along. A road census in 1904 showed about 2,000,-000 miles of public highway in the United States. About 100,000 miles of these were covered with gravel, 40,000 with macadam, none with concrete. The rest were dirt.

Among the first to push for better roads was the American Automobile Association which was organized in 1902 to help the motorist. To publicize the need for better roads, the AAA, in 1905, sponsored a tour from New York through New England and back. It was called the Glidden Tour after Charles J. Glidden who contributed a trophy to be awarded the winner. It was not a race, in that speed did not count. Points were awarded on the basis of a car's reliability.

46

The best known cars in America participated. Through mud, rain, billowing dust, over rickety wooden bridges and up steep hills, the tourists made their way. Fenders were smashed, axles broke, tires blew out. In one town, local police arrested eight contestants for breaking the speed limit. In Connecticut, a hole in the road caused one passenger to be thrown from a car. In Massachusetts, a passenger fell out of another car when it accidentally skidded.

The winner of the first Glidden Tour was a Pierce Great Arrow. But this was less significant than the public attention which the tour brought to the state of America's roads. Improvement was slow at first, but speeded up as others joined the AAA's drive. In 1916, Congress passed the Federal Highway Act. As cities and states increased their own road budgets, the beginnings of an American road system, capable of handling the growth of car production, was under way.

Early motorists contended with bad driving conditions as well as temperamental engines.

America's Favorite Car

Henry Ford was a farm boy who was fascinated by machines. He tinkered with watches long before he tinkered with engines. He experimented with steam engines before he studied Otto's internal-combustion engine. In 1896, when he was working as an engineer at the Edison Illuminating Company in Detroit, he built his first car. It was a crude vehicle which he built by himself in his spare time. It ran well enough for Ford to quit his job and devote his time exclusively to building automobiles.

Winton's success in racing convinced Ford that speed was the way to attract attention. If he could beat Winton his name would be known all over the country. And that is exactly what he did, not once, but several times. First he did it with a two-cylinder car, and then in the most famous early racer of all, "999", which he owned jointly with a friend, Tom Cooper.

The victory of Henry Ford's "999" over the Winton "Bullet" in the 1902 race at Grosse Pointe, Michigan brought national attention to the automobile and to the man who would revolutionize manufacturing and industrial methods in this country.

Ford's racing car had four cylinders which developed eighty horsepower, an extraordinary amount in those days. To drive it, Ford called on Barney Oldfield, America's champion bicycle racer. Oldfield had never driven a car, but he was eager to try. Ford made one concession to Oldfield's bicycle experience. He installed a two handed steering device which looked like bicycle handlebars.

In 1902, on a three mile track at Grosse Pointe, Michigan, Oldfield roared into a lead over Winton's "Bullet" and stayed there. He won by half a mile. The victory did what Ford hoped it would do—it brought him to the attention of men who had money to form a company to build the kind of car he had in mind. Twice before he had formed companies: the first, in 1899, was the Detroit Automobile Company which made 20 cars. It failed late in 1900. The second was the Henry Ford Company which later became the Cadillac Automobile Company after Ford withdrew from it. The third firm established was the Ford Motor Company. Henry Ford was made vice president and general manager at a salary of $3,000 a year. Before the end of 1903, the first of what would be millions of Fords was on the market. It was the Model A, rated at eight horsepower, which sold for $800. For $100 extra, it would be delivered with rear seats.

For the next five years a variety of Fords came on the market, one selling for as low as $500. This was the Model N which weighed only 700 pounds. No four cylinder car had ever sold for so little in the United States and it was an immediate success. From 1906 to 1908 Ford tried to capture both the high and low priced markets. In addition to the Model N, he offered the six cylinder Model K at $2,800. At this time a one cylinder Cadillac could be bought for a trifle less than $1,000.

Ford's big car did not sell. But, the company had a hard time keeping up with the orders for the Model N. Henry Ford reached the obvious conclusion. The automobile was no longer a rich man's plaything. Its future belonged to all Americans. Ford decided that what they were looking for was an inexpensive, reliable car—easy to run and easy to maintain. Starting in 1908, and continuing for nineteen years, the Ford Motor Company was to provide that car: the Model T.

In 1908 the Model T Ford was introduced, and after a slow start, soon

The light-weight Ford Model N Runabout cost only $500 in 1906.

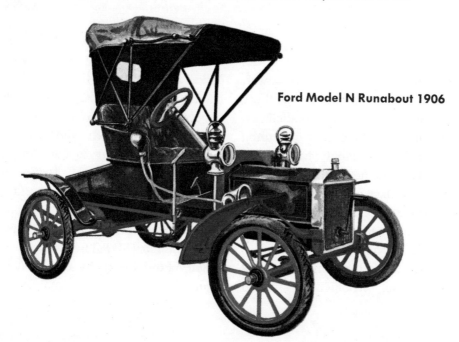

Ford Model N Runabout 1906

Ford Model T

With the Model T Ford came an era when cars were no longer considered rich men's toys.

dominated the international automobile world. The last Model T came off the assembly line at the Ford plant in May, 1927. There had been more than 15,000,000 cars of its kind, a record which no car before or since has matched. In the nineteen years of production there had been gradual changes in body design in order to be able to reduce its selling price, as well as minor modifications in the engine and transmission. But the original Model T was never changed in any of its basic factors, and it never failed to meet its original standards: inexpensive reliability.

The first Model T Ford was a four cylinder, open touring car selling for $850. In 1926, the last full year of production, a two seater runabout sold for $260. Balloon tires were $25 extra, and a self-starter and demountable rims were $85 extra.

The car's engine generated 22.5 horsepower. It was cast in one piece, an innovation which gave it strength and durability. Its transmission was operated by planetary gears—two speeds forward, operated by a foot pedal, plus reverse operated by another pedal. In an emergency, reverse could be used as a brake. This often gave the impression of riding a bucking bronco, but it was effective. The Model T had its steering wheel on the left hand side of the car—and there it has stayed on all cars. Up to that time, its position had varied depending on the manufacturer's preference.

The Model T was an instant success. Production started late in 1908, and only 300 were built. This was a trickle which became a torrent. As Ford perfected the assembly line which permitted the cars to be put together with speed and accuracy, production increased. By 1920, nearly a million cars a year were being turned out. In 1923 there were two million.

One of the advantages of the Model T which endeared it to its owners was Ford's insistence on interchangeable parts. This was necessary to make his assembly line work properly. To the Ford owner, interchangeable parts meant that replacements could always be found when needed. They were available at mail order houses and local hardware stores as well as in service stations.

Owners, especially farmers, put the Model T to a variety of uses which Henry Ford could not have foreseen. Special wheels permitted it to be used as a tractor to plow the fields. With the rear jacked up, the Model T's turning wheels could generate electricity to run other farm equipment. Some farmers cut away the back of the body, installed a strong floor board, and had an excellent farm truck. It was indeed, as Ford called it, "The Universal Car." But five millions of owners and non-owners usually called it a "tin lizzie."

The Model T had a number of faults which alternately irritated and amused its owners. The gasoline tank was under the driver's seat. There was no gas gauge. To check the tank, or to fill it, the driver and passenger had to leave the car and remove the seat. The Model T was difficult to start in cold weather, and many ingenious methods were devised to solve this. Filling the radiator with hot water was supposed to help. So was jacking up the rear end to permit the wheels to run freely. Sometimes the gas did not flow to the engine when the car was going up hill. When that happened, people backed up.

A car as cheap as the Model T carried no extras. In its lifetime, more than 5,000 items were put on the market, all advertised as improvements on the basic car. They ranged from entire bodies for $68.75 ("a real nifty, classy up-to-the-minute speedster body") to a lock for 29 cents. Many things we consider standard equipment today were lacking. A big business was done in bumpers, luggage racks, speedometers, shock absorbers and rear view mirrors.

The Model T inspired songs (including one called "The Love Story of the Packard and the Ford"), poetry, and thousands of jokes. It appeared in dozens of movies, especially comedies, and always created laughs. No one was more amused at the jokes than Henry Ford himself. Every joke sold a car, he said. Whether that was true or not, the Model T made the world car-conscious. It had worked a revolution in American life. It had not only spanned the period from the horse and buggy age to the automobile age; it had helped bring that change about. It was both the last of the early cars and the first of the modern cars.

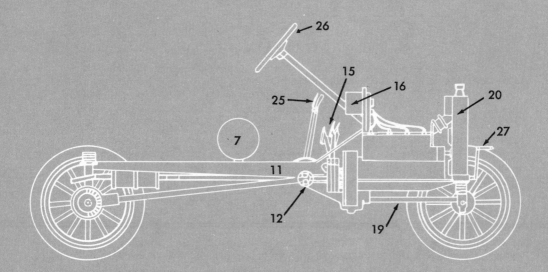

1. hub brake assembly
2. differential gear
3. rear spring
4. muffler
5. drive shaft
6. exhaust pipe
7. gasoline tank
8. rear axle radius rod
9. emergency brake
10. brake pull rod
11. frame
12. universal joint
13. transmission
14. magneto

15. pedals
16. coils
17. dash
18. steering post
19. front radius rods
20. radiator
21. steering gear rods
22. engine
23. front axle
24. front spring
25. hand levers
26. steering wheel
27. hand crank

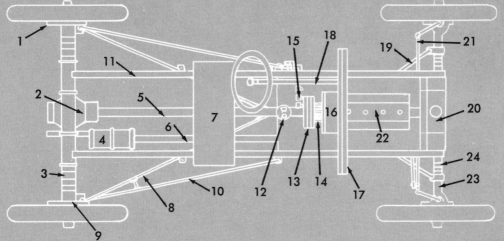

Index

CREDITS: p. 27, 35 (top), Courtesy The New York Public Library; p. 31 (top and center), 33 (top), 34 (top), 42, 46, 50, Courtesy The Albert Meacham Collection of the Long Island Automotive Museum, Southampton, L. I., New York; p. 24, 25, 26, Courtesy The Smithsonian Institution, Washington, D.C.

A